Core Knowledge Language Arts®

Unit 5
Workbook

Skills Strand
GRADE 2

Amplify learning.

Core Knowledge®

ISBN 978-1-61700-223-6

Printed in the USA
07 LSCOW 2020

Unit 5
Workbook

This Workbook contains worksheets that accompany many of the lessons from the Teacher Guide for Unit 5. Some of the worksheets in this book do not include written instructions for the student because the instructions would have contained nondecodable words. The expectation is that teachers will explain these worksheets to the students orally, using the guidelines in the Teacher Guide. The Workbook is a student component, which means that each student should have a Workbook.

Name _____

Dear Family Member,

Below you will find our spelling words for this week. We are beginning to learn how to put words in alphabetical order using just the first letter of each word.

The worksheet your child has for homework should be completed in this way:

1. On the back of this page, have your child write the alphabet down the side of the paper.

2. Have your child read all of the words aloud and circle the first letter in each word.

3. Ask your child to write each set of words in alphabetical order.

quickly	neatly	ugly	jelly	chilly
slowly	funny	angry	empty	mommy
daddy	happy	pretty	grumpy	

Tricky Word: alphabet

Please continue to encourage your child to read at least 20 minutes every night. At this point in the school year, your child should be able to self-select reading material and read independently for the entire 20 minutes.

A
_____
_____
_____
Z

quickly neatly ugly alphabet	jelly chilly slowly
1. _____	1. _____
2. _____	2. _____
3. _____	3. _____
4. _____	4. _____
funny angry empty mommy	daddy happy pretty grumpy
1. _____	1. _____
2. _____	2. _____
3. _____	3. _____
4. _____	4. _____

Word Sort

Sort the words by spelling. Write the words with the /u/ sound spelled 'u'
under *bug*. Write the words with the /u/ sound spelled 'o' under *other*.

~~rush~~	trust	bunch	son
month	ugly	mother	until
truck	unkind	money	front

/u/spelled 'u'   /u/ spelled 'o'
as in *b<u>u</u>g*   as in *<u>o</u>ther*

rush

_____   _____

_____   _____

_____   _____

_____   _____

_____   _____

_____   _____

_____   _____

Fill in the Blank

Write the best word from the box to complete each sentence.

mother	cover	month	money	wonder
dozen	trumpet	grumpy	mummy	thunder

1. We heard the _____ before we saw the lightning.

2. My _____ , not my Dad, woke me up this morning.

3. I wish I had some _____ to buy some candy.

4. I feel _____ when I don't get plenty of sleep.

5. King Tut's _____ was discovered in 1922.

6. Did you _____ your nose when you sneezed?

7. The _____ is a brass instrument.

8. Did you know that 12 cookies make one _____?

The Beginning

Long before you were born, in a place we can no longer find, there was a king. King Alfred was his name.

King Alfred was in charge of a large land that stretched from the dark forests of the north to the sea in the south. The people of this land were very happy with him as their king. King Alfred liked to have fun. He liked parties and feasts. He was fair and kind, and he kept his people safe.

King Alfred could not do this all by himself. He had twelve knights to help him keep his lands peaceful and his people safe. These brave knights— well, sometimes they were brave— helped to keep bad things from happening.

The most well-known knight of all was Sir Gus the Fearless. The king himself had given Sir Gus the name "Fearless." This was an odd name, for Sir Gus was not entirely fearless. In fact, he had a lot of fears.

Sir Gus was scared of the dark. He was scared of mice and bats and spiders. He did not like boats and he could not swim. Shadows and loud noises made him faint. In fact, lots of things made Sir Gus faint.

Sir Gus had all the things a knight must have. He had a shield and a lance. He had a spear and a sword. But Sir Gus liked a long soak in a bathtub better than a fight.

Cats and horses made Sir Gus itch. Sometimes the itching was so bad that he would start jumping up and down.

Sir Gus was rather absentminded. He got lost a lot and could rarely tell which way to go. Sir Gus found it difficult to get up in the morning. He liked to sleep in, so he was late most of the time.

All in all, Sir Gus was a rather odd knight. But King Alfred did not see this. What he saw was that Sir Gus always served him well.

The Beginning

1. Why are the people of King Alfred's land happy with King Alfred as their king?

_____

_____

_____

_____

2. Who helps King Alfred keep his lands peaceful and his people safe?

_____

_____

_____

_____

3. What are some of Sir Gus's fears?

_____

_____

_____

_____

Family Member Directions: Ask your child to answer each question using a complete sentence.

4. What are some of your fears?

_____

_____

_____

_____

5. Why might cats and horses make Sir Gus itch?

_____

_____

_____

_____

6. What do you think of Sir Gus?

_____

_____

_____

_____

Fill in the Blank

younger	none	welcome
gloves	enormous	touched

1. Is your sister older or _____ than you?

2. When it is cold, I cover my hands with _____.

3. The mat on the porch said "_____."

4. If you eat it all, there will be _____ left for me.

5. An antonym of "tiny" is "_____."

6. The baby cried after she _____ the hot stove.

Write two new sentences using any two of the words from the box.

_____

_____

_____

_____

Directions: Have students read the words in the box aloud. Students should write the best word from the box to complete each sentence.

nervous	dove	country
love	shove	poisonous

1. We looked up and saw a white _____ flying by.

2. I like hamburgers, but I really _____ ice cream!

3. Mexico is a _____.

4. It's not nice to hit or _____.

5. When I have to take a test, I get _____.

6. Some spiders and snakes are _____.

Write two new sentences using any two of the words from the box.

_____

_____

_____

_____

The Thief

One dark and stormy night while King Alfred was sleeping, a thief crept into his bedroom and stole the king's golden ring. The next morning, when the king woke up, he saw that his ring was gone!

The king was very sad.

"Someone stole my ring!" he cried in agony. "It was my father's ring, and his father's before him. It is a king's ring. I must have it back!"

King Alfred was so upset in the morning; he could not eat his herring on toast.

King Alfred summoned his twelve brave knights. Eleven of them came at once on horseback. Sir Gus the Fearless came later, on foot. Sir Gus explained why he was late. He explained that he had lost his horse.

"Why, good sir," said the king, "you will not get very far on foot!"

"Yes, my lord. I mean no, my lord," replied Sir Gus. "The problem is, your majesty, that when I am on my horse, I itch. I had such a bad itch last night that I fell off my horse and it ran off."

"Well, you must stop itching then," said the king.

"Yes, indeed," replied Sir Gus, trying very hard not to itch.

Then the king told the knights what had happened. He told them he was counting on them to recover his ring.

The next day, at sunrise, eleven of the knights galloped off to find the thief.

Some time after lunch, Sir Gus was awakened by the king himself.

"Not up yet?" asked the king.

"Pardon me, my lord," stammered Sir Gus. "I was just…"

"Nevermind!" said the king. "There's no need to explain. Why should you be up at the crack of dawn? For what can a knight do without a horse? But never fear! I have a gift for you. You may take my horse. But you must be careful, Sir Gus. My horse is the fastest in the land."

Sir Gus got out of bed. He stretched and yawned loudly. Then he got dressed.

"Do not fear," said Sir Gus, as he mounted the horse. "I am an—"

And with that, Sir Gus was carried off. The king's horse had shot off like an arrow.

The Thief

TAKE
HOME

Family Member Directions: Have your child reread the story and answer the questions using complete sentences.

1. What is a thief?

    _____

    _____

    _____

    _____

2. Sir Gus takes longer to get to the king than the other knights. Why?

    _____

    _____

    _____

    _____

3. Why did Sir Gus fall off his horse?

    _____

    _____

    _____

    _____

4. Why isn't the king mad when he finds Sir Gus sleeping in?

_____

_____

_____

_____

All's Well That Ends Well

Sir Gus rode the king's horse out into the country. He galloped over green land and lovely rolling hills.

All was well, until he began to itch. He scratched his leg. He scratched his neck. He tried to scratch his back and nearly fell off the horse. Nothing seemed to help. At last Sir Gus told himself he had better stop, lest he scratch himself right off the king's horse!

Sir Gus stopped in front of a farmhouse. Near the farmhouse was a stone well. Standing near the well was a young, strong-looking man.

Sir Gus spoke to the young man politely. "Pardon me, good sir," he said, "may I drink from your well?"

"Yes, you may," said the young man.

Sir Gus went to draw water from the well. He grabbed the rope and began to tug on it. But then he felt the need to scratch. He let go of the rope and started scratching himself. Soon he was itching himself so hard that he started jumping up and down. He jumped up and down so much that he fell into the well and landed with a splash at the bottom.

"Ack!" cried Sir Gus. "What have I done?"

It was a good thing that Sir Gus was tall. The water in the well only came up to his chest.

The young man peered down into the well.

"Have no fear!" he shouted to Sir Gus. "I will help you. I will drop the bucket down. Take hold of it, and I will lift you up."

Sir Gus waited nervously at the bottom of the dark well. He did not like the dark or the cold water. His legs began to shiver and shake.

The bucket came down the well. Sir Gus grabbed the bucket and held on tight.

Slowly the young man began to bring Sir Gus up out of the well.

As Sir Gus reached the top of the well, the young man offered the knight his hand.

"Young man," said Sir Gus, as he stepped out of the well, "I am touched by your generous deed. I would like to thank you for helping me. What is your name?"

"My name is Robin," replied the man.

"Well, then, Robin," said Sir Gus, "I thank you."

"You are welcome," said Robin.

The two men shook hands. Robin clasped the knight's hand so tightly that water dripped from his glove.

Robin smiled. "Come into my house," he said. "I will find you some dry clothing."

Sir Gus went inside.

"Sit down," said Robin. "I will fetch you some dry clothing and something to drink." Robin left the room.

Sir Gus sat down on a wooden chair. As he did so, a large black cat jumped onto his lap. At once, Sir Gus began to itch all over. He got up and started jumping up and down. He jumped so hard that he knocked over a chair and bumped into a shelf.

Some things fell off the shelf. As he bent down to pick these things up, Sir Gus spotted a ring. It was the king's ring! Robin was the robber!

Sir Gus stood thinking for a moment.

"There is no point fighting with the man," Sir Gus said to himself. "That would be dangerous. I can tell by his grip that he is very strong."

Sir Gus grabbed the ring. Then he tiptoed quietly out of the house. He mounted his horse and rode back to see the king.

Well

1. _____

_____

_____# _____

Well

2. _____

_____

_____# _____

Well

3. _____

_____

_____# _____

Dear Family Member,

The words shown below contain the /u/ sound, written with various spellings, all of which your child has studied at school. Ask your child to read the words. Then ask your child to use each word in an oral sentence.

but	some	other	just	such
come	mother	under	done	money
brother	southern	touch	run	young
trouble	month	son	none	bus

Name _____

Spelling Test

1. _____   9. _____

2. _____   10. _____

3. _____   11. _____

4. _____   12. _____

5. _____   13. _____

6. _____   14. _____

7. _____   15. _____

8. _____

_____

_____

_____

Write the words in alphabetical order.

1. _____

2. _____

3. _____

Sound Spellings

This chart shows 4 spellings for the /u/ sound. Use the chart to fill in
Worksheet 5.3.

	'u'	'o'	'ou'	'o_e'
b	buddy buzz	brother	boisterous	become
c	cup	cover	cousin country	
d	duck	dozen	Doug	done dove
e			enormous	
f	fun	front	famous	
g			generous	glove
h	hug	honey	hideous	handsome
j	junk just		jealous	
l	lunch			
m	must mug mud	money monkey mother		
n	nun	nothing	nervous	none
p	puppy			
r	run			
s	such sudden sun	son	southern	shove some something
t	truck trust	ton	touch	
u	unless until			
w		won		
y	yuck		young	

Use the chart on Worksheet 5.2 to fill in the blanks.

1. Count the words on the chart that have the sound /u/ spelled 'u' and write the number here. _____

2. Count the words on the chart that have the sound /u/ spelled 'o' and write the number here. _____

3. Count the words on the chart that have the sound /u/ spelled 'ou' and write the number here. _____

4. Count the words on the chart that have the sound /u/ spelled 'o_e' and write the number here. _____

5. Which spelling for /u/ has the most words?

   _____

6. Which word on the chart names something bees make?

   _____

7. Which word on the chart means twelve of something?

   _____

8. Which word on the chart is a synonym for good-looking?

   _____

9.   Which word on the chart is a synonym for cup?

_____

10. Which word on the chart is an antonym for old?

_____

11. Which word on the chart is a synonym for mom?

_____

12. Which word on the chart is a proper noun?

_____

13. Which word on the chart is a synonym for finished?

_____

14. Write a sentence using at least two words from the chart:

_____

_____

_____

The Hungry Troll

1. When Sir Gus brings the king his ring, the king is…

    A. delighted

    B. angry

    C. sad

2. What wakes King Alfred?

    A. thunder

    B. the cries of a baby

    C. the cries of a troll

3. Sir Tom says that trolls are scared of…

    A. water

    B. fire

    C. thunder

4. Where does Sir Gus go when the rest of the knights ride off to find the troll?

    A. Sir Gus goes to the shed to find a weapon.

    B. Sir Gus goes to the barn to find a horse.

    C. Sir Gus goes to the kitchen to get a snack.

Directions: Students should select the best answer for each question.

5.   Which Sir Gus story have you liked best so far? Why?

_____

_____

_____

_____

_____

_____

_____

_____

_____

Dear Family Member,

This week all of your child's spelling words include the /ie/ sound (long vowel sound of the letter 'i'). In some words the /ie/ sound of the letter 'i' is spelled with the letters 'igh'. In other words it is spelled with 'y'.

Please help your child to work with their alphabetizing skills by completing the back of this worksheet.

Just as you did last week, please follow these directions:

1. Have your child write the alphabet down the side of the paper.

2. Have your child read all of the words aloud and circle the first letter in each word.

3. Ask your child to write each set of words in alphabetical order.

knight	might	high	right	frightened
light	bright	crying	pry	why
nearby	trying	sky	drying	

Tricky Word: kingdom

Put the words in each box in alphabetical order.

A
___
___
___
___
___
___
___
___
___

knight might high drying	right trying sky kingdom
1. _____	1. _____
2. _____	2. _____
3. _____	3. _____
4. _____	4. _____
frightened light bright crying	**pry why nearby**
1. _____	1. _____
2. _____	2. _____
3. _____	3. _____
4. _____	

Z

Sound Spellings

Read aloud all the words in each column. Circle the spelling in each word for the sound shown at the top of the column.

/u/	/ee/	/ie/
fuzzy	kidney	slime
shove	cookie	silent
sponge	cream	right
touch	athlete	lied
shrug	piece	satisfy
month	prefix	mind
mother	chief	frying
love	stories	fight
until	greed	pride
cousin	field	satisfied

Parts of Speech

Find examples of the following parts of speech in "The Hungry Troll" and write them on the lines, along with the page number for each answer.

1. common noun: _____ Page:_____

2. proper noun naming a person: _____ Page:_____

3. proper noun naming a person: _____ Page:_____

4. common noun: _____ Page:_____

5. common noun naming a place: _____ Page:_____

6. common noun naming a thing: _____ Page:_____

7. adjective: _____ Page:_____

8. adjective and a noun: _____ Page:_____

9. verb: _____ Page:_____

10. verb "to be": _____ Page:_____

Use some of the words from the list on the front of the worksheet to make up your own sentence or silly story.

_____

_____

_____

_____

_____

_____

The Spelling Spoilers

Choose one character. Write adjectives to describe the character. First, write the adjectives from the text. Then, write some adjectives of your own. Last, write two sentences using some of the adjectives you listed.

Sir Gus

_____

_____

_____

_____

_____

_____

_____

Troll

_____

_____

_____

_____

_____

_____

_____

_____

Fill in the Blank

Read the words in the box aloud. Then write the best word from the box to complete each sentence.

afraid	adults	telescope
appetite	about	orange

1. My parents are both _____.

2. I eat a lot. I have a big _____.

3. Doug looks at the stars with his _____.

4. Should we paint the walls yellow or _____?

5. Is your book _____ a king and queen?

6. I am not _____ of the dark.

Write two new sentences using two of the words from the box.

_____

_____

_____

_____

Name _____

Beat the Spoilers

The Spelling Spoilers are trying to wreck your spelling. Your teacher will say some words. Foil the Spoilers by spelling the words correctly.

	Copy	Spell	Did you beat the Spoilers?	
1.			○ yes	○ no
2.			○ yes	○ no
3.			○ yes	○ no
4.			○ yes	○ no
5.			○ yes	○ no
6.			○ yes	○ no

Copy	Spell	Did you beat the Spoilers?	
		○ yes	○ no
7.		○ yes	○ no
8.		○ yes	○ no
9.		○ yes	○ no
10.		○ yes	○ no

Fire!

Write the answer to each question using complete sentences.

1. Why was it not hard to find the troll?

   _____

   _____

   _____

2. Sir Tom's plan changed a bit when Sir Gus appeared. How did it change?

   _____

   _____

   _____

3. Do you think that Sir Tom really thinks that Sir Gus is the bravest knight? Why or why not?

   _____

   _____

   _____

   _____

4.   What happened when Sir Gus fainted?

_____

_____

_____

_____

5.   List 4 nouns from the story "Fire!"

_____   _____

7.   List 4 verbs from the story "Fire!"

_____   _____

_____   _____

8.   List 4 adjectives from the story "Fire!"

_____   _____

_____   _____

Fire!

It was not hard to find the troll. Trolls cry when they are hungry. The knights simply followed the sound of loud sobs and eating.

As nightfall neared, the knights arrived at the foot of a large hill. The troll had spent all day eating the rocks and plants on the hill. All that was left on the hill were some prickly plants and some old, dying trees.

Near the top of the hill was a cave. Scary troll sounds were coming from inside the cave.

The knights met in a grove at the foot of the hill. They knelt down and made a plan.

"When it is dark we will light our torches," said Sir Tom. "Then we will creep up the hill. The sight of the flames will scare the troll and it will go back to its home beneath the ground."

"And what if that plan fails?" asked Sir Ed. "I don't care to be the troll's dinner."

"Well, do you have a better plan?" asked Sir Tom.

Sir Ed said nothing. The other knights were quiet, as well.

At that very moment came the sound of a horse trotting nearby.

"Found you at last!" said Sir Gus as he rode up to the knights. "So, my fellow knights, tell me, have you devised a plan of attack to defeat this monstrous troll?"

"Yes, we have!" said Sir Tom. "We have agreed that our bravest knight will creep up the hill with a torch and frighten the troll away."

"Splendid idea!" said Sir Gus. "And who is going to attempt this brave deed?" he asked, looking around.

"You!" said Sir Tom and Sir Ed together.

"But, but… well… I… er… um…," said a reluctant Sir Gus.

It was no good trying to get out of it. Sir Tom handed Sir Gus a lit torch. Then he pointed at the cave.

Sir Gus went up the hill alone. By the time he reached the mouth of the cave, it was pitch black. The lit torch cast shadows on the ground.

Sir Gus looked around him. He saw shadows dancing on the ground. He was afraid. But he pressed on.

From inside the cave came alarming troll sounds.

"Snnniccck, Snnnuummm, Guffumffffff!"

The troll was eating bits of rock with its sharp teeth, then spitting out the bits it did not like.

Sir Gus approached the cave. Small pieces of rock came flying out. Some of them landed at Sir Gus's feet. Sir Gus jumped back, trying to avoid the flying pieces of rock.

Suddenly there was a thumping sound. Thump! Thump! Thump! The troll was coming out of the cave!

As the troll got closer, the sounds got louder.

"SNNNNICCCK, SNNNUUUUMMMM, GUFFUMFFFFFF!"

Sir Gus was afraid. He started to feel weak in the knees. At last he fainted. His torch fell to the ground. It landed on some dry, prickly plants near the mouth of the cave. The plants caught on fire. The flames got bigger quickly.

From inside the cave came a scream. Then came the thumping sound of a large beast running away. Soon, all that remained was the sound of crackling flames.

Sir Gus lay on the ground for a while. At last the heat from the fire woke him. He got up and ran back down the hill.

When Sir Gus appeared, the knights shouted, "Hooray! Brave Sir Gus lit the fire! He has driven away the troll! Hooray for Sir Gus!"

Subject and Predicate

Underline the subject once and the predicate twice. Put a check above any compound subject or predicate.

1. The boys and girls played in the mud.

2. Ben and Jim like to draw and color pictures.

3. Jamie and Jesse like to run and jump.

4. Linda rides a bike.

5. Kelly can pick and eat grapes.

6. Henry the pig eats his food at night.

7. Clementine feeds her 12 piglets.

8. Clementine and Henry are good pig parents.

9. Joe the turkey likes to visit and sit with Clementine, Henry, and the piglets.

10. Joe struts around the pig pen each morning.

The Boat Trip

Briefly summarize what happened in the story "The Boat Trip."

_____

_____

_____

_____

_____

Draw lines between the subjects and predicates showing what happened in the story.

Subjects	Predicates
King Alfred	went hunting with the king
Eleven knights	became seasick
Sir Gus	insisted that his knights go sailing with him

Reviewing Contractions

Write the two words used to make each contraction.

Example: can't	can not
don't	
it's	
I'm	
you're	
we're	
isn't	
aren't	

Write a sentence using at least one of the contractions.

_____

_____

_____

_____

Write the contraction that can be made from the two words.

that is	that's
you are	
is not	
that will	
could not	
are not	
we are	
they are	

Write a sentence using at least one of the contractions.

_____

_____

_____

_____

Name _____

Spelling Test

1. _____   9. _____

2. _____   10. _____

3. _____   11. _____

4. _____   12. _____

5. _____   13. _____

6. _____   14. _____

7. _____   15. _____

8. _____

_____

 _____

_____

Write the words in alphabetical order.

1. _____

2. _____

3. _____

Writing Sentences

Write three different sentences. Make sure your sentence fits with the !, ?, or . at the end of the line.

1. _____

_____

_____!

2. _____

_____

_____?

3. _____

_____

_____.

Dear Family Member,

Below you will find our spelling words for this week. All of the words have the sound of /ee/ (also known as long e) spelled with the letters 'ie'. We are continuing our work learning to alphabetize words. As the next step in this skill, we are learning to use the alphabet as a reference tool and less as a matching tool for letters.

Just as you did last week, please follow these directions:

1. Have your child read all of the words aloud and circle the first letter in each word.

2. Ask your child to write words in alphabetical order.

3. You may find it helpful for your child to number the words in the box before writing them in alphabetical order. It is easier to erase a number than a word.

field	piece	shield	thief	kitties
achieve	relief	grief	yield	movie
niece	cookies	ladies	babies	

Tricky Word: water

Put the words in each box in alphabetical order.

A

field piece shield thief kitties achieve relief	grief yield movie niece cookies ladies babies water
1. _____	1. _____
2. _____	2. _____
3. _____	3. _____
4. _____	4. _____
5. _____	5. _____
6. _____	6. _____
7. _____	7. _____
	8. _____

Z

Sound Sort

Sort the words by spelling. Write the words that have the 'ul' ending under *useful*. Write the words that have the 'al' ending under *metal*. Write the words that have the 'il' ending under *April*.

~~harmful~~	fossil	hospital	evil
total	pencil	several	awful
peaceful	hopeful	normal	civil

'ul'	'al'	'il'
as in *useful*	as in *metal*	as in *April*

harmful

_____ _____ _____

_____ _____ _____

_____ _____ _____

_____ _____ _____

_____ _____ _____

_____ _____ _____

_____ _____ _____

The King's Ghost

"Ar! Do as we say or die!" came the sound of a large booming voice from somewhere on the water.

King Alfred and eleven of his knights jumped with fright. They had all tried to sail the boat in the stormy waves and strong winds. They looked up to see a pirate ship flying a black flag. The pirate ship had sailed up next to the king's boat.

The king and the eleven knights were not prepared to fight. The knights did not have their swords or shields with them.

"I will count to ten," shouted the pirate chief. "If you do not hand over the king and his boat by then, we will attack! We do not care to harm you, but if we must, then we must!"

The pirate chief began to count, "One, two . . . um." He hesitated. (Pirates aren't good at math!)

"Three," came a voice from below. It was Sir Gus. He was lying down below the deck, and he was feeling very ill.

Sir Gus was so ill that he had no idea what was happening. The strong winds had kept him from hearing what the pirate chief had said. All he could make out was the sound of someone counting.

"Thank you," said the pirate chief. He went on counting. "Seven, eight, nine . . ."

"Uuuuuug! Ooooooe!" came a loud and scary sound from inside King Alfred's boat.

"Uuuuuug! Ooooooe!"

"What is that hideous sound?" yelled the pirate.

"It is the ghost of our last king, and it protects our ship!" replied Sir Tom.

Sir Tom was well aware that, in fact, the hideous sound was coming from Sir Gus, who was feeling very sick indeed, but he was hoping to scare the pirates away with a ghost story.

"Uuuuuug! Ooooooe!" came the sound again.

"If you harm the king," Sir Tom shouted, "you will be haunted by this evil, vengeful ghost! I will count to ten, and you had better go away, you thief! The ghost would rather not harm you, but if it must, then it must."

Pirates are very afraid of ghosts. And so, within seconds, the pirate ship began to sail away.

Not long after, the clouds cleared and the waves died down. Sir Gus felt some relief and came limping back up on deck.

"Well done, Sir Gus!" said the king. "You scared those evil pirates away by pretending to be a ghost."

"I did?" said Sir Gus, still looking rather green in the face.

"Why, yes!" said the king. "Such a clever and helpful trick! How can I ever repay you for your wisdom and bravery? Perhaps I should award you a medal?"

"Your majesty," said Sir Gus, "the best payment of all would be if you would order the captain to sail this boat back to land. I find the nautical life not to agree with me."

And with that, the king's boat sailed for home.

The King's Ghost

1. What made King Alfred and his knights jump with fright?

    _____

    _____

    _____

2. Why couldn't the king and his knights defend themselves?

    _____

    _____

    _____

3. What did the pirate say would happen if the king and his boat were not handed over?

    _____

    _____

    _____

4. Who did the pirates think was making the loud, scary sound?

_____

_____

_____

5. Do you think you would have been fooled by Sir Tom's trick? Why or why not?

_____

_____

_____

_____

6. Who do you think should have gotten credit for saving the day? Why?

_____

_____

_____

Fill in the Blank

Write the best word from the box to complete each sentence.

about	China	around	Africa	appetite
Tennessee	love	cousin	something	touch

1. _____ is a country in the Far East.

2. _____ is a state in our country.

3. Your aunt's child is your _____.

4. Do not _____ a hot stove!

5. I worked up an _____ by chopping wood for the fire.

6. _____ is a continent.

7. Can you tell me _____ your book?

8. Let's look _____ the room for the lost book.

9. I _____ to eat snow cream in winter.

10. I have _____ to say about that.

Write the following correctly.

1. dr john smith _____(4)

2. january 3 2011 _____(2)

3. are you ready to go _____(2)

4. is mrs betty white your mother

    _____(6)

Write the word that means more than one.

5. man _____

6. woman _____

7. butterfly _____

8. box _____

9. goose _____

Circle the nouns, draw an arrow from the adjective to the noun, and draw a wiggly line under the verb in each sentence.

10. The old man walked.

11. The tiny girl ran.

12. A green frog jumped.

13. A tall tree fell.

14. The blue sky darkened.

Draw one line under the subject and two lines under the predicate.

15. Frank and Joe ran the marathon.

16. Lisa ate ice cream and cake.

17. Fay and Mike like to swim.

18. Larry and Debbie walked and ran six miles.

19. Linda and Ernie will train for the swim meet.

Dear Family Member,

The words shown below all end with 'le'. Please help your child practice reading these words. Ask your child to use each word in an oral sentence after he or she reads it.

single	handle	gamble	temple
stable	cradle	idle	twinkle
able	title	needle	apple
gurgle	jingle	cattle	purple
bubble	eagle	steeple	beagle

Fill in the Blank

Write the best word from the box to complete each sentence.

mother	camel	decide	jungle	cousin
petals	bubble	afraid	wonderful	

1. Could you help me _____ between a cookie or a cupcake?

2. I call my _____ , "mom."

3. It was a _____ party and we all had fun!

4. An animal with two humps is a _____.

5. I have a night light because I am _____ of the dark.

6. Monkeys live in the _____.

7. The rose _____ were scattered in front of the bride.

8. I like to blow a big _____ with my gum.

9. My _____ and aunt will come to spend the night.

Choose the best word from the box to complete each sentence.

cover	animals	fossils
angels	chief	little

10. The baby bird is too _____ to fly.

11. A zoo has a lot of _____.

12. Will you _____ the dish before you place it in the fridge?

13. Some of the _____ were from long, long ago.

14. The leader of a Native American tribe is often called a _____.

15. Some people believe that _____ have wings.

Parts of Speech

Find examples of these parts of speech in "The Boat Trip" and write them on the lines.

common noun: _____

proper noun: _____

proper noun naming a person: _____

common noun: _____

common noun naming a place: _____

common noun naming a thing: _____

adjective: _____

adjective and a noun: _____

verb: _____

verb *to be*: _____

Use at least one noun and one verb from the list to make up your own sentence or silly story. Underline the subject once and the predicate twice.

_____

_____

_____

_____

_____

_____

_____

_____

_____

Name _____

Fill in the Blank

Write the best word from the box to complete each sentence.

bubble	apples	beagles	noodles	eagle
maple	single	candle	poodles	stable

1. A horse will stay in the _____ on a rainy day.

2. Mom likes to light a _____ on the table at supper.

3. A _____ leaf is on the Canadian flag.

4. _____ and _____ are kinds of dogs.

5. I like to blow a big _____ with my gum.

6. Would you like to help me pick _____ from the tree?

7. An _____ is a symbol of our country.

8. I like to eat spaghetti _____.

9. I can't eat just one _____ chip. I like to eat the entire bag.

Write adjectives for Sir Gus showing his condition in this story. First, write the adjectives in the text. Then, write some adjectives of your own. Next, write two complete sentences using some of the adjectives you listed. Last, on the back of this page, make a sketch of Sir Gus, illustrating your adjectives.

Sir Gus

_____

_____

_____

_____

_____

_____

_____

_____

_____

Spelling Test

1. _____   9. _____

2. _____   10. _____

3. _____   11. _____

4. _____   12. _____

5. _____   13. _____

6. _____   14. _____

7. _____   15. _____

8. _____

_____

_____

_____

Write the words in alphabetical order.

1. _____

2. _____

3. _____

4. _____

5. _____

Fill in the Blank

Write the best word from the box to complete each sentence.

station	~~options~~	attention
infection	dictionary	vacation

1. Select one of the following __**options**__ .

2. If you don't know what a word means, you can look it up in the

    _____ .

3. This summer, we will take a _____ .

4. If you don't clean that cut, you might get an _____ .

5. We need to stop at a gas _____ .

6. If you want to understand, you should pay _____ .

Write the best word from the box to complete each sentence.

reflection	lotion	potion
invention	stationery	emotions

1. The witch is making a sleeping _____.

2. If you look in the pond, you will see your _____ staring back at you.

3. Carol wrote the letter on _____.

4. To keep your skin from drying out, use _____.

5. Jealousy and anger are _____.

6. The wheel is a great _____.

Dear Family Member,

These are our spelling words for this week. Once again, we are asking you to help your child put the words in alphabetical order. Any additional time you can spend practicing alphabetizing during the week will help your child master this skill.

yelled	yarn	yellow	yes	myth
symbol	system	cry	frying	satisfy
yawn	sticky	lying	energy	

Tricky Word: edge

yelled system edge lying myth	yarn symbol cry frying energy
1. _____	1. _____
2. _____	2. _____
3. _____	3. _____
4. _____	4. _____
5. _____	5. _____

Name _____

Fill in the Blank

Write the best word from the box to complete each sentence.

hospital	helpful	petals	animal
cheerful	emergency	appear	dangerous

1. In an _____, call 911.

2. The rose _____ smell great!

3. She is always smiling and _____.

4. It would be _____ to me if you would clean your room.

5. My favorite _____ is a panda.

6. She is a nurse in a _____.

© 2013 Core Knowledge Foundation

Write the best word from the box to complete each sentence.

pedal	decide	April	America
signal	principal	dangerous	equals

1. The month after March is _____.

2. I can't _____ if I would like red or pink ribbons.

3. Two plus two _____ four.

4. We live in the United States of _____.

5. It is very _____ to skate on thin ice.

6. Turn left at the next traffic _____.

The Fearsome Beast

Read all of the sentences first and then number them in order.

_____ The fearsome beast ran into the Dark Dismal Swamp and sank in the mud.

_____ The bandits had dinner and went to sleep.

_____ The bandits fled.

_____ The bandits grabbed Sir Gus, tied him up, and tossed him into the back of their wagon.

_____ The fearsome beast tried to attack Sir Gus.

_____ A hunter untied Sir Gus.

_____ The fearsome beast was blinded by the sunlight that bounced off Sir Gus's helmet.

_____ The bandits arrived at the Bleak Forest of the East.

The Past-Tense Ending –*ed*

Most verbs can be changed from the present to the past tense by adding the suffix –*ed*.

I start	I **started**
I want	I **wanted**
I need	I
I point	I
I paint	I
I plant	I

Sometimes the –*ed* suffix is sounded /e/ + /d/, as it is in the words you just made. But sometimes it is sounded /d/.

I call	I **called**
I open	I **opened**
I follow	I
I show	I
I seem	I
I yell	I

Sometimes the suffix _–ed_ is sounded /t/.

we ask	we **asked**
we pass	we **passed**
we pick	we
we finish	we
we jump	we
we pack	we

Which sound (or sounds) do we say at the end of the past-tense verbs listed?

1. played	○ /e/ + /d/	✓ /d/	○ /t/
2. sprinted	○ /e/ + /d/	○ /d/	○ /t/
3. rushed	○ /e/ + /d/	○ /d/	○ /t/
4. filled	○ /e/ + /d/	○ /d/	○ /t/
5. shouted	○ /e/ + /d/	○ /d/	○ /t/
6. watched	○ /e/ + /d/	○ /d/	○ /t/

All of these verbs are in the _____ tense.

    ○   present

    ○   past

Planning Sheet: New Story Ending

1. What if _____

    _____

    _____?

2. What if _____

    _____

    _____?

3. What if _____

    _____

    _____?

4. What if _____

    _____

    _____?

5. What if _____

    _____

    _____?

Editing Checklist

Ask yourself these questions as you edit your draft.

1. Do I have a title?	
2. Do I have an ending that makes sense?	
3. Do all of my sentences start with uppercase letters?	
4. Do all of my sentences end with a final mark? (. ? or !)	
5. Have I checked to see if I spelled all of my words correctly?	

The short story on this page has words with many of the new spellings from this unit. Read this story aloud to a family member.

My younger brother, Jeremy, is a very serious person. He spends tons of time alone in his room studying. He rarely attends parties or agrees to do things with other kids. I sometimes wonder about the benefit of acting like that. I suppose Jeremy will probably go to college someday. Then he'll have a better chance to get a good job and make lots of money as an adult. With a little luck, I bet he could become rich!

Read the words in the box aloud, and then put them in alphabetical order.

serious	college	wonder
person	brother	rarely

1. _____

2. _____

3. _____

4. _____

5. _____

6. _____

Fire!

Sir Gus went up the hill alone. By the time he reached the mouth of the cave, it was pitch black. The lit torch cast shadows on the ground.

Sir Gus looked around him. He saw shadows dancing on the ground. He was afraid. But he pressed on.

From inside the cave came alarming troll sounds.

"Snnniccck, Snnnuummm, Guffumffffff!"

The troll was eating bits of rock with its sharp teeth, then spitting out the bits it did not like.

Sir Gus approached the cave. Small pieces of rock came flying out. Some of them landed at Sir Gus's feet. Sir Gus jumped back, trying to avoid the flying pieces of rock.

Suddenly there was a thumping sound. Thump! Thump! Thump! The troll was coming out of the cave!

As the troll got closer, the sounds got louder.

"SNNNNICCCK, SNNNUUUUMMMM, GUFFUMFFFFFF!"

Planning Sheet: New Story Ending

1. What if _____

   _____

   _____?

2. What if _____

   _____

   _____?

3. What if _____

   _____

   _____?

4. What if _____

   _____

   _____?

5. What if _____

   _____

   _____?

The King's Birthday

Briefly explain what King Alfred had planned for his birthday party.

_____

_____

_____

_____

_____

Draw lines showing who said what.

"Winning will be our
birthday gift to you, Sire!"   King Alfred

"And happy Birthday to me!"   Sir Tom

"We will make them cry!"   Sir Pete

"We are the most feared
knights of all time."   Sir Tom

The King's Birthday

Six months passed until King Alfred saw his knights. This time he did not need their help, but he asked them to come to his birthday party. The king had asked 500 people to join him. He had made plans for a large feast, as well as jousting, magic, and dancing. Everyone was very excited.

The palace was filled with five thousand candles. Gold cloth was draped on the walls. King Alfred had planned a treat for everyone. Just as the jousting was about to begin, a thousand white doves were to be released into the sky above the palace.

King Alfred asked King Henry, the king of another kingdom, to attend the birthday party. The twelve knights were coming too. King Henry's knights were going to challenge King Alfred's knights in jousting. The winners would get 100 gold coins each.

On the day of the party, the king met with some of his knights.

"This is going to be the best party ever!" said the excited king. "I am eager to see each of you joust. I think King Henry and his knights will be amazed by your skill."

"Winning will be our birthday gift to you, Sire!" said Sir Pete.

"We are the most feared knights of all time!" said Sir Tom. "We will crush them! We will make them cry!"

Sir Gus looked on as his fellow knights boasted of their skill. He did not join them. In fact, he was very nervous. He was hoping that he would not start itching and fall off his horse.

"I know you will win," said the king. "And that will make a fine birthday present. I thank you in advance!"

The knights began to file out.

"Sir Gus!" called the king.

"Your majesty?" said Sir Gus.

"Do you like my birthday cake?" asked the king.

"Yes, Sire."

"Do you see how the royal baker made a tiny king out of icing that looks just like me?"

"Yes, Sire."

"It is a wonderful birthday present! But the best present of all will be seeing you defeat Sir Ivan the Black Knight in the jousting."

"Sir Ivan?" asked Sir Gus nervously.

"Yes," said the king. "He has made quite a fearsome name for himself. But I trust you will beat him."

Sir Gus was too scared to speak.

"Well, then," said the king. "Off you go! And happy birthday to me!"

The Future Tense

Change the present tense to the future tense.

present tense	future tense
I swim.	I will swim.
I sleep.	
I fish.	
I eat.	
I dress.	

Finish the sentence, and write what you will do when you grow up.

<u>**When I grow up I will...**</u> _____

_____

_____

_____

_____

_____

_____

_____

Name _____

New Ending

Story Title:_____

_____

_____

_____

_____

_____

_____

_____

_____

_____

_____

_____

_____

Editing Checklist

Ask yourself these questions as you edit your draft.

1. Do I have a title?	
2. Do I have an ending that makes sense?	
3. Do all of my sentences start with uppercase letters?	
4. Do all of my sentences end with a final mark? (. ? or !)	
5. Have I checked to see if I spelled all of my words correctly?	

Spelling Test

1. _____   9. _____

2. _____   10. _____

3. _____   11. _____

4. _____   12. _____

5. _____   13. _____

6. _____   14. _____

7. _____   15. _____

8. _____

_____

_____

_____

Write the words in alphabetical order.

1. _____

2. _____

3. _____

4. _____

5. _____

Name _____

First, circle all of the words ending in *–tion*. (There are 8.) Then, on the back of the sheet, put these same words in alphabetical order.

ATTENTION: Volcano has shown signs of a possible eruption. Please use extreme caution while visiting the park.

Be advised that inhalation of volcanic ash can lead to breathing difficulty. As a precaution, do not get within three miles of the volcano. Note that it is a violation of state laws to get within one mile of the volcano—no exceptions. (A ranger station is located at the one-mile marker.)

---

1. _____

2. _____

3. _____

4. _____

5. _____

6. _____

7. _____

8. _____

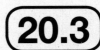

Planning Sheet: New Story Ending

1. What if _____

   _____

   _____?

2. What if _____

   _____

   _____?

3. What if _____

   _____

   _____?

4. What if _____

   _____

   _____?

5. What if _____

   _____

   _____?

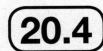

New Ending

Story Title:_____

_____

_____

_____

_____

_____

_____

_____

_____

_____

_____

_____

_____

_____

Editing Checklist

Ask yourself these questions as you edit your draft.

1. Do I have a title?	
2. Do I have an ending that makes sense?	
3. Do all of my sentences start with uppercase letters?	
4. Do all of my sentences end with a final mark? (. ? or !)	
5. Have I checked to see if I spelled all of my words correctly?	

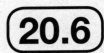

Betrayed

Answer each question using complete sentences.

1. What two things made the people gasp?

    _____

    _____

2. Who knocked Sir Basil to the ground?

    _____

    _____

3. Describe Sir Ivan.

    _____

    _____

4. Why didn't Sir Gus get up after Sir Ivan knocked him to the ground?

    _____

    _____

5. If you had to joust, would you be scared? Why or why not?

_____

_____

6. List 4 nouns from "Betrayed."

_____   _____

_____   _____

7. List 4 verbs from "Betrayed."

_____   _____

_____   _____

8. List 4 adjectives from "Betrayed."

_____   _____

_____   _____

Dear Family Member,

The spelling words this week all have either 'le', 'el', or 'tion' as part of the word. Additionally, we are asking your child to alphabetize all of the words. By now, your child should be fairly proficient at this task and able to complete it without looking at the alphabet. However, we would encourage you to ask your child to use the alphabet as a checking tool when the task is complete.

turtle	bundle	pickle	shuffle	cattle
label	angel	gravel	jewel	fiction
education	inspection	motion	question	

Tricky Word: schwa

turtle	bundle	pickle	shuffle	cattle
label	angel	gravel	jewel	fiction
education	inspection	motion	question	

1. _____

2. _____

3. _____

4. _____

5. _____

6. _____

7. _____

8. _____

9. _____

10. _____

11. _____

12. _____

13. _____

14. _____

Sound Sort

Write the words with the tricky spelling 'a' sounded /a/ under *bad,* the words with the tricky spelling 'a' sounded /ae/ under *acorn,* and the words with the tricky spelling 'a' sounded /ə/ under *about.*

that	crazy	lady	around
alike	stand	appear	table
baby	and	happen	

sounded /a/

as in *bad*

_____

_____

_____

_____

_____

_____

_____

_____

sounded /ae/

as in *acorn*

_____

_____

_____

_____

_____

_____

_____

_____

sounded /ə/

as in *about*

_____

_____

_____

_____

_____

_____

_____

_____

The Wizard

Answer each question using complete sentences.

1. Who is Albert?

   _____

   _____

2. What is a wizard?

   _____

   _____

   _____

3. What is a synonym for "wicked"?

   _____

4. What is an antonym for "wicked"?

   _____

5. How can the wizard's spell be broken?

   _____

   _____

6. Would you rather have a king like King Alfred or a king like King Henry? Why?

_____

_____

_____

Illustrate something that happened in the story, and write some sentences explaining your illustration.

_____

_____

_____

_____

Name _____

Tricky 'a'

'a'	→ /a/	hat	band	last
	→ /ae/	paper	later	lady
	→ /ə/	about	along	balloon

Sort the underlined words with Tricky Spellings.

		/a/ as in *hat*	/ae/ as in *paper*	/ə/ as in *about*
1.	Spring comes <u>after</u> winter.			
2.	<u>Can</u> you set the <u>table</u>?			
3.	She told him to go <u>away</u>.			
4.	Let's get some books from the small <u>bookcase</u>.			
5.	<u>What</u> do you like?			
6.	<u>Take</u> out the <u>trash</u>.			
7.	Let's <u>have</u> eggs for lunch.			
8.	This envelope needs a <u>stamp</u>.			

Tricky 'e'

The letter 'e' can stand for three sounds. It can stand for /e/ as in *bed*, /ee/ as in *me*, or /ə/ as in *debate*. Each sentence below has a word with an underlined 'e'. Which of the three sounds do you hear in each word?

1. His best race is the 100-m<u>e</u>ter dash.

    A. /e/ as in *bed*

    B. /ee/ as in *me*

    C. /ə/ as in *debate*

2. The m<u>e</u>n mixed up a batch of cement.

    A. /e/ as in *bed*

    B. /ee/ as in *me*

    C. /ə/ as in *debate*

3. I have a bug bite on my <u>e</u>lbow.

    A. /e/ as in *bed*

    B. /ee/ as in *me*

    C. /ə/ as in *debate*

4. When I was fifteen I went on a trip to <u>E</u>gypt.

    A. /e/ as in *bed*

    B. /ee/ as in *me*

    C. /ə/ as in *debate*

5. That night we stayed in a hot<u>e</u>l.

    A. /e/ as in *bed*

    B. /ee/ as in *me*

    C. /ə/ as in *debate*

6. When I saw the sticky glop on my plate, I lost my app<u>e</u>tite.

    A. /e/ as in *bed*

    B. /ee/ as in *me*

    C. /ə/ as in *debate*

7. Can you keep a s<u>e</u>cret?

    A. /e/ as in *bed*

    B. /ee/ as in *me*

    C. /ə/ as in *debate*

8. Dad is sick. He is running a f<u>e</u>ver.

    A. /e/ as in *bed*

    B. /ee/ as in *me*

    C. /ə/ as in *debate*

9. Miss Douglas, I did not understand the l<u>e</u>sson.

    A. /e/ as in *bed*

    B. /ee/ as in *me*

    C. /ə/ as in *debate*

Breaking the Spell

1. What does Sir Gus hear when he awakes?

    A. his horse

    B. the wizard

    C. doves

2. What is it that Sir Gus sees upon waking up?

    A. He sees the people clapping and cheering.

    B. He sees the people sleeping.

    C. He sees the people gasping.

3. Where is it that the Black Knight carries the king?

    A. to the dungeon

    B. to the throne room

    C. to the kitchen

4. What wakes the king?

    A. Sir Gus yelling to wake up

    B. a spider crawling on him

    C. the web of a male garden spider touching his left hand

5. Write some sentences describing the dungeon.

_____

_____

_____

_____

_____

6. Find examples of these parts of speech in the story:

Adjectives	Proper Nouns	Common Nouns	Verbs

Tricky 'e'

First read the words. Then, write the words with the tricky spelling 'e' sounded /e/ under *send*, the words with the tricky spelling 'e' sounded /ee/ under *behind*, and the words with the tricky spelling 'e' sounded /ə/ under *debate*.

~~pebble~~	abdomen	mention	she
algebra	relic	symmetry	metallic
equal	pencil	lesson	refill

sounded /e/ as in *send*	sounded /ee/ as in *behind*	sounded /ə/ as in *debate*
pebble		

Tricky 'o'

Write the words with the tricky spelling 'o' sounded /o/ under *stop*, the words with the tricky spelling 'o' sounded /oe/ under *hotel*, and the words with the tricky spelling 'o' sounded /u/ under *from*. Sort only the words in which the 'o' is underlined.

Last m<u>o</u>nth, my <u>o</u>lder br<u>o</u>ther w<u>o</u>n sec<u>o</u>nd place in a h<u>o</u>t dog-eating c<u>o</u>ntest. To win, he had to eat the m<u>o</u>st hot dogs. Well, my brother ate lots and lots of hot dogs— most of the people competing found it imp<u>o</u>ssible to eat as many. At the cl<u>o</u>sing ceremony, my brother was given a t<u>o</u>n of money (one thousand in cash) and a tr<u>o</u>phy of a g<u>o</u>lden hot dog. My brother slipped the m<u>o</u>ney in his p<u>o</u>cket and smiled m<u>o</u>destly as people took his snapsh<u>o</u>t. It was a fine m<u>o</u>ment for my brother.

sounded /o/ as in *stop*	sounded /oe/ as in *hotel*	sounded /u/ as in *from*
		month
_____	_____	_____
_____	_____	_____
_____	_____	_____
_____	_____	_____
_____	_____	_____
_____	_____	_____
_____	_____	_____

Choose one character from Sir Gus. Record all the adjectives you can find from the Reader on the left side. Think about 5 more adjectives of your own and list them on the right side. Then write 5 sentences describing the character using some of your adjectives. Make sure you have complete sentences with both subjects and predicates.

Name of the character from Sir Gus:

_____

Adjectives from the text:

_____

_____

_____

_____

_____

_____

_____

_____

Adjectives you thought of:

_____

_____

_____

_____

_____

_____

_____

_____

Your sentences:

_____

_____

_____

_____

_____

_____

_____

_____

_____

_____

_____

_____

_____

_____

_____

Tricky 'o'

Sort the words by sound. Write the words that have 'o' sounded /o/ under hop. Write the words that have 'o' sounded /oe/ under open. Write the words that have 'o' sounded /u/ under son.

'o'					
	→	/o/	hop	drop	spot
	→	/oe/	open	hotel	no
	→	/u/	son	front	coming

		/o/ as in hop	/oe/ as in open	/u/ as in son
1.	I need to find my father and <u>mother</u>.			mother
2.	I have one sister and two <u>brothers</u>.			
3.	Is the watch silver or <u>gold</u>?			
4.	The baby has a <u>bottle</u>.			
5.	Is my ankle sprained or <u>broken</u>?			
6.	When I broke my leg, I went to the <u>hospital</u>.			
7.	This is a difficult math <u>problem</u>.			

Sound Sort

Sort the words by sound. Write the words that have 'o_e' sounded /oe/ under home. Write the words that have 'o_e' sounded /u/ under come.

'o_e' → /oe/	home	those	wrote
→ /u/	come	none	love

		/oe/ like home	/u/ like come
1.	We can leave when we are <u>done</u>.		**done**
2.	Adam is wearing <u>gloves</u>.		
3.	Alan is digging a <u>hole</u>.		
4.	Do you want all of the bacon or just <u>some</u> of it?		
5.	Her youngest <u>son</u> went skiing down the <u>slope</u>.		
6.	Take small bites <u>so</u> you don't <u>choke</u>.		
7.	Simon tied a knot in the <u>rope</u>.		

Revenge

Summarize the story "Revenge."

_____

_____

_____

_____

_____

_____

Match the character to the action.

_____ King Alfred   A. betrayed King Alfred

_____ King Henry   B. fell off his chair

_____ Sir Gus   C. hoped to lead the king's army

_____ Eleven knights   D. sent an army to fight King
                                          Henry's army

**Bonus: Draw a rectangle around the column that includes predicates.
Draw a circle around the column that includes subjects.**

Sound Sort

First read the words in the box. Write the words with the tricky spelling 'o_e' sounded /oe/ under *hope* and the words with the tricky spelling 'o_e' sounded /u/ under *done*.

~~role~~	welcome	notebook	shove
glove	vote	none	choke
lovely	rope	bone	stole

sounded /oe/
as in *hope*

role

_____

_____

_____

_____

_____

_____

sounded /u/
as in *done*

_____

_____

_____

_____

_____

_____

Spelling Test

1. _____   9. _____

2. _____   10. _____

3. _____   11. _____

4. _____   12. _____

5. _____   13. _____

6. _____   14. _____

7. _____   15. _____

8. _____

_____

_____

_____

Write the words in alphabetical order.

1. _____

2. _____

3. _____

4. _____

5. _____

Tricky 'ou'

Write the words that have the tricky spelling 'ou' sounded /ou/ under
shout **and the words that have the tricky spelling 'ou' sounded /u/ under**
touch.

'ou' →	/ou/	shout	out	mountain
	/u/	touch	country	jealous

		/ou/ as in shout	/u/ as in touch
1.	Is he old or <u>young</u>?		**young**
2.	The sky has lots of <u>clouds</u>.		
3.	The lake is <u>enormous</u>.		
4.	Did you hear that <u>sound</u>?		
5.	My <u>cousin's</u> name is <u>Doug</u>.		
6.	Tests make me <u>nervous</u>.		
7.	Check the lost and <u>found</u> box.		

Battle Plans

Answer each question using complete sentences.

1. The king thinks that Sir Gus has volunteered to lead the army.
    Why?

    _____

    _____

    _____

2. What does Sir Tom hand to Sir Gus?

    _____

    _____

    _____

3. What is the real reason that Sir Gus holds the map upside
    down?

    _____

    _____

    _____

4. Why do you think Sir Gus chooses to attack at night?

_____

_____

_____

5. At the end of the story, why are Sir Ed and Sir Tom happy?

_____

_____

_____

6. Are you like Sir Ed, or are you like Sir Gus? Explain.

_____

_____

_____

"Marching Orders"

1. What is Sir Gus cooking when Sir Doug arrives?

   A. frogs and toads

   B. eggs and bacon

   C. grits and greens

2. What does Sir Doug tell Sir Gus?

   A. You need to cook more eggs.

   B. Sir Tom and Sir Ed want bacon.

   C. Sir Tom and Sir Ed need your help.

3. Why did Sir Tom and Sir Ed need help?

   A. The night attack did not go well.

   B. The army needed breakfast.

   C. The bridge was broken.

4. Who sent Sir Doug to get help?

   A. the Black Knight

   B. Sir Gus

   C. Sir Tom and Sir Ed

5. Why were Sir Doug and the rest of the men puzzled?

    A. Sir Gus told the knights to ride in the wrong direction.

    B. Sir Gus was eating breakfast.

    C. Sir Gus did not have a map.

6. Why does Sir Doug think it would be better to cross the river than to march over the bridge?

    A. It is faster to cross the river.

    B. The bridge is broken.

    C. The horses like to drink the water.

7. Why did Sir Gus say it was too dangerous to cross the river?

    A. Sir Gus wants to swim later.

    B. Sir Gus doesn't know how to swim.

    C. Sir Gus did not want the horses to get wet.

8. Number these sentences in the correct order.

_____ Sir Gus wanted to cross the river at the bridge.

_____ Sir Gus was dressed for battle.

_____ Sir Gus was cooking breakfast.

_____ Sir Gus and his men set off.

Grammar Assessment

Write the following correctly.

1. dr joe white   _____ (4)

2. mrs bonnie black   _____ (4)

3. june 3 2011   _____ (2)

4. 801 east high street new canton virginia

    _____

    _____ (7)

5. wednesday   _____ (1)

Write the word that means more than one.

6. mouse   _____

7. fox   _____

8. dragonfly _____

9. tool   _____

10. goose   _____

Circle the nouns, draw an arrow from the adjective to the noun, and draw a wiggly line under the verb in each sentence.

Example: The famous (writer) talked.

11. The little boy runs.

12. The fat cat sleeps.

13. A pink flower bloomed.

14. A tall tree grew.

15. The pretty lady rushed.

Draw one line under the subject and two lines under the predicate.

Example: Ted rode his bike and played ball.

16. Scott and Matt worked on the book.

17. Jim and James ate cake and ice cream.

18. Bobby and Fay will train and work out.

19. Chester and Clementine ran around the barnyard.

20. Paula and Jane will plant flowers.

Circle the correct tense for each verb.

21. I will run later.   past   present   future

22. I jumped rope.   past   present   future

23. I see.   past   present   future

24. Jane walked.   past   present   future

25. Ted hugged.   past   present   future

26. Susan cried.   past   present   future

27. Roger will taste the cake.   past   present   future

28. James will race Jim.   past   present   future

29. Joe sits.   past   present   future

30. I will play this afternoon.   past   present   future

Decoding

Circle the word your teacher calls out.

1.   across   amount   amiss   claws

2.   hasn't   haven't   hadn't   he'll

3.   mom   mother   brother   bother

4.   determine   deduct   define   decide

5.   shove   shut   shovel   shoot

6.   able   apple   ample   apply

7.   native   notion   nation   national

8.   funny   fundamental   fulfill   funnel

9.   copper   cuddle   couple   cable

10. cousin   copies   cupful   cotton

Circle the word your teacher calls out.

1.   traction   fraction   faction   addition

2.   above   about   avoid   amend

3.   fabulous   dangerous   dangers   dagger

4.   wonderland   wistful   wonderful   wondering

5.   glove   lovely   love   clove

6.   hide   hideout   hidden   hideous

7.   peel   pebble   puddle   petal

8.   missile   dismissal   fizzle   fossil

9.   cheerful   hopeful   helpful   careful

10.   animate   animal   annual   anything

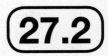

The Final Battle

Number the sentences in the correct order or sequence.

____ The Black Knight told his men to stand down.

____ King Henry's army retreated.

____ Sir Gus and his men reached the Old Stone Bridge.

____ Sir Gus's men shouted, "Hooray for Sir Gus!"

____ Sir Gus and his men charged at King Henry's army.

____ Sir Gus and his men rested.

____ The Black Knight's men tossed their shields and weapons aside.

____ Sir Gus and his men fought King Henry's army.

Write the sentences from above in the correct order or sequence.

1. _____

_____

2. _____

_____

3. _____

_____

4. _____

   _____

5. _____

   _____

6. _____

   _____

7. _____

   _____

8. _____

   _____

Alphabetizing Assessment

Put the following words in alphabetical order:

across	mother	decide	shove
nation	funnel	couple	traction
wonderful	hideous	petal	love

1. _____   7. _____

2. _____   8. _____

3. _____   9. _____

4. _____   10. _____

5. _____   11. _____

6. _____   12. _____

Directions: Place an x in the box of any word read incorrectly by the student. If possible, write what the student says in the box.

Feature						Number Incorrect?
'o' > /u/	mother	brother	front	won	son	
'o_e' > /u/	love	glove	done	none	come	
'ou' > /u/	cousin	touch	young	southern	country	
'a' > /ə/	about	alike	afraid	China	America	
'e' > /ə/	debate	decide	category	hello	decay	
'al' > /ə/ + /l/	total	metal	animal	royal	signal	
'ul' > /ə/ + /l/	helpful	cheerful	wonderful	hopeful	careful	
'il' > /ə/ + /l/	evil	April	devil	fossil	nostril	
'le' > /ə/ + /l/	apple	little	uncle	jungle	table	
'tion'	station	vacation	emotion	nation	fiction	
tricky 'a'	bandit	alone	wall	later	band	
tricky 'e'	lemon	rewind	me	debate	test	
tricky 'o'	copper	open	from	hotel	no	
tricky 'o_e'	home	some	wrote	cone	come	
tricky 'ou'	shout	touch	pound	country	out	

Directions: Place an X beside any word that the student misses, and, if possible, write what the student says in place of the correct word.

always	around	because	been	before
best	both	but	call	cold
does	don't	fast	first	five
found	gave	goes	green	its
made	man	off	or	pull
read	right	sing	sit	sleep
tell	their	these	those	upon
us	use	very	wash	which
why	wish	work	would	write
your				

Total number correct out of 46 _____

Tricky Spelling 'a'

Write the words that have the tricky spelling 'a' sounded /a/ under *hat*, the words that have the tricky spelling 'a' sounded /ae/ under *paper*, and the words that have the tricky spelling 'a' sounded /u/ under *about*.

'a'				
→	/a/	hat	band	last
→	/ae/	paper	later	lady
→	/ə/	about	along	balloon

	/a/ as in *hat*	/ae/ as in *paper*	/ə/ as in *about*
1. She has a yellow <u>cap</u>.			
2. She is wearing her silver <u>necklace</u>.			
3. To mail this letter, I need one <u>stamp</u>.			
4. When my mom cooks, she wears her <u>apron</u>.			
5. I need a <u>map</u> to find the park.			

	/a/ as in *hat*	/ae/ as in *paper*	/ə/ as in *about*
6. When will Tommy <u>a</u>rrive?			
7. This horse needs its s<u>a</u>ddle.			
8. I think the best month is <u>A</u>pril.			

Color Sort

If a square has a word with the letter 'a' sounded /a/, make it red.
If a square has a word with the letter 'a' sounded /ae/, make it yellow.
If a square has a word with the letter 'a' sounded /ə/, make it green.
If a square has a word with the letter 'a' sounded /aw/, make it orange.

after	about	began	family	around
matter	affect	talk	taken	cannot
radio	apple	perhaps	idea	avoid
rather	having	village	carry	cake
ability	chapter	small	China	strange

Word Sort

Write the words with the tricky spelling 'a' sounded /a/ under *bad*, the words with the tricky spelling 'a' sounded /ae/ under *acorn*, the words with the tricky spelling 'a' sounded /ə/ under *about*, and the words with the tricky spelling 'a' sounded /o/ under *water*.

~~giant~~	lasted	faking	chapter
waffle	extra	alone	able
actress	orange	apple	want

sounded /a/	sounded /ae/	sounded /ə/
as in *bad*	as in *acorn*	as in *about*
		giant
_____	_____	_____
_____	_____	_____
_____	_____	_____
_____	_____	_____
_____	_____	_____
_____	_____	_____
_____	_____	_____

Tricky Spelling 'a'

The letter 'a' can stand for 4 sounds. Which sounds does it stand for in the underlined letters in these words?

Al_a_ska
- ✓ /a/ as in *cat*
- ○ /a/ as in *table*
- ○ /ə/ as in *about*
- ○ /aw/ as in *wall*

_A_merica
- ○ /a/ as in *cat*
- ○ /ae/ as in *table*
- ○ /ə/ as in *about*
- ○ /aw/ as in *wall*

t_a_lk
- ○ /a/ as in *cat*
- ○ /ae/ as in *table*
- ○ /ə/ as in *about*
- ○ /aw/ as in *wall*

Can_a_da
- ○ /a/ as in *cat*
- ○ /ae/ as in *table*
- ○ /ə/ as in *about*
- ○ /aw/ as in *wall*

Abr_a_ham
- ○ /a/ as in *cat*
- ○ /ae/ as in *table*
- ○ /ə/ as in *about*
- ○ /aw/ as in *wall*

banan_a_
- ○ /a/ as in *cat*
- ○ /ae/ as in *table*
- ○ /ə/ as in *about*
- ○ /aw/ as in *wall*

Ar_a_bia
- ○ /a/ as in *cat*
- ○ /ae/ as in *table*
- ○ /ə/ as in *about*
- ○ /aw/ as in *wall*

Alman_a_c
- ○ /a/ as in *cat*
- ○ /ae/ as in *table*
- ○ /ə/ as in *about*
- ○ /aw/ as in *wall*

Afric_a_
- ○ /a/ as in *cat*
- ○ /ae/ as in *table*
- ○ /ə/ as in *about*
- ○ /aw/ as in *wall*

Tricky Spelling 'e'

'e'	→	/e/	pet	left	letter
	→	/ee/	me	rewind	legal
	→	/ə/	debate	appetite	strategy

		/e/ as in *pet*	/ee/ as in *me*	/ə/ as in *debate*
1.	He is singing the National <u>Anthem</u>.			**Anthem**
2.	This glass is <u>empty</u>.			
3.	Dad and I saw a play at the <u>theater</u>.			
4.	I need a carton of <u>eggs</u>.			
5.	Have you <u>seen</u> Paila			
6.	The balloon is filled with <u>helium</u>.			
7.	We have <u>tickets</u> to go to the circus!			

Name _____

Color Sort

If a square has a word with the letter 'e' sounded /e/, make it red.
If a square has a word with the letter 'e' sounded /ee/, make it yellow.
If a square has a word with the letter 'e' sounded /ə/, make it green.

children	send	began	system	wanted
himself	second	decay	me	report
open	equal	given	hello	started
problem	parent	moment	legal	deposit
except	decide	subject	she	hundred

Tricky Spelling 'o'

Write the words that have the tricky spelling 'o' sounded /o/ under *hop*, the words that have the tricky spelling 'o' sounded /oe/ under *open*, and the words that have the tricky spelling 'o' sounded /u/ under *son*.

'o' →		/o/	hop	drop	model
	→	/oe/	open	hotel	no
	→	/u/	son	front	coming

		/o/ as in *hop*	/oe/ as in *open*	/u/ as in *son*
1.	There are 31 days in the <u>month</u> of March.			month
2.	The kids are eating <u>popsicles</u>.			
3.	When he swims, he wears <u>goggles</u>.			
4.	Rats, mice, and hamsters are <u>rodents</u>.			
5.	I like reading <u>poetry</u>.			
6.	She is reading a <u>novel</u>.			
7.	The horses <u>galloped</u> past us.			

Word Sort

Write the words with the tricky spelling 'o' sounded /o/ under *stop*, the words with the tricky spelling 'o' sounded /oe/ under *hotel*, and the words with the tricky spelling 'o' sounded /u/ under *from*.

~~front~~	pollen	open	hoping
cover	model	kingdom	motel
command	topic	noble	tropical

sounded /o/
as in *stop*

sounded /oe/
as in *hotel*

sounded /u/
as in *from*

front

_____   _____   _____

_____   _____   _____

_____   _____   _____

_____   _____   _____

_____   _____   _____

_____   _____   _____

_____   _____   _____

_____   _____   _____

Name _____

Color Sort

If a square has a word with the letter 'o' sounded /o/, make it red.
If a square has a word with the letter 'o' sounded /oe/, make it yellow.
If a square has a word with the letter 'o' sounded /u/, make it green.

motel	only	person	across	total
money	cannot	problem	over	coming
also	going	process	almost	modern
reason	potted	product	program	provide
bodies	solid	brother	most	radio

Sound Sort

Write the words that have the tricky spelling 'o_e' sounded /oe/ under *home*, and the words that have the tricky spelling 'o_e' sounded /u/ under *come*.

'o_e'		/oe/	h**o**me	th**o**se	tromb**o**ne
	→	/u/	c**o**me	n**o**ne	l**o**ve

		/oe/ like *home*	/u/ like *come*
1.	Even if you are mad, you should not <u>shove</u>.		shove
2.	I like ice cream <u>cones</u>.		
3.	That is not the letter I <u>wrote</u>.		
4.	The mat on the porch said "<u>Welcome</u>!"		
5.	Do you want a slice, or do you want the <u>whole</u> thing?		
6.	A rock is a lot like a <u>stone</u>.		
7.	I <u>love</u> my baby sister.		

Color Sort

If the space has a word with the spelling 'o_e' sounded /oe/, make it red. If the space has a word with the spelling 'o_e' sounded /u/, make it yellow.

those	become	home	whole	undone
rose	alone	stone	wrote	lovely
hope	gloves	closely	bones	shove
some	suppose	nose	handsome	drove
zone	envelope	lonely	none	propose

Tricky Spelling 'ou'

Write the words that have the tricky spelling 'ou' sounded /ou/ under *shout,* and the words that have the tricky spelling 'ou' sounded /u/ under *touch.*

'ou' → /ou/	shout	out	proud
→ /u/	touch	country	jealous

		/ou/ as in *shout*	/u/ as in *touch*
1.	When he got an A, and I got a B, I felt <u>jealous</u>.		**jealous**
2.	Stop being silly. It's time to be <u>serious</u>.		
3.	The cookie is flat and <u>round</u>.		
4.	They are sitting on the <u>couch</u>.		
5.	David is my uncle, and Rachel is my <u>cousin</u>.		
6.	The radio is too <u>loud</u>!		
7.	When she is upset, she <u>pouts</u>.		

Word Sort

**Write the words with the tricky spelling 'ou' sounded /ou/ under *mouth*
and the words with the tricky spelling 'ou' sounded /u/ under *touch*.**

~~outing~~	serious	dangerous	about
amount	southern	cousin	shouting
youngster	thousand	background	counter

sounded /ou/
as in *mouth*

sounded /u/
as in *touch*

outing

_____   _____

_____   _____

_____   _____

_____   _____

_____   _____

_____   _____

_____   _____

Circle all of the words you can find ending in /sh/ /ə/ /n/, including the two already circled for you; you should find 16 words in all.

Voice 1: "Attention. Secret Agent 009! How is the expedition going?"

Voice 2: "It's going well."

Voice 1: "Can you hear me okay?"

Voice 2: "Yes, I hear you. The reception is good."

Voice 1: "What is your position?"

Voice 2: "I am in section 7, next to those tall rock formations."

Voice 1: "Roger, Agent 009. There is an old volcano at that location. There is not much danger of an eruption, but use caution just the same."

Voice 2: "Roger. What are my options? Should I go south?"

Voice 1: "No. There is a lot of thick vegetation in that direction. Head north to the junction. Then go left. You will pass the old railroad station. Then you will see an old plantation house. The owner is on vacation. We will pick you up there."

Fill in the Blank

Lots of adjectives end in *-ous*. **Write the best words from the box to complete each sentence.**

enormous	~~nervous~~	poisonous
hideous	famous	jealous

1. Look at his hands shaking before he goes on stage. He must be more _____**nervous**_____ than you.

2. Don't drink that stuff. It could make you very sick because it is _____.

3. Ben has the best bike. I wish I had one just like it. I feel so _____.

4. Ever since she was on that TV show, she has become very _____.

5. That drawing is so ugly. It's _____.

6. That giant is so big. He's _____.

Name _____

Circle the Sounds

Circle the letters in each word that stand for the vowel sound.

young	none
month	Doug
done	come
front	some
the	won
was	ton
touch	a
what	glove
love	monk
son	shove

Match the Picture

Mark the sentence that matches what you see.

	☑ She is young. ○ She is not young.
	○ That snake is poisonous. ○ That spider is poisonous.
	○ That's a lot of honey. ○ That's a lot of money.
	○ The lion is resting. ○ The monkey is resting.
	○ She is wearing a dress. ○ She is wearing pants.
	○ A dove is in the pond. ○ A duck is in the pond.
	○ That's a carnival. ○ That's a cardinal.

	○ There is an apple on the table. ○ There is a bottle on the table.
	○ She's eating a pretzel. ○ She's eating a pickle.
	○ The kid has a fossil. ○ The kid has a pencil.
1 + 4 = 5	○ This is addition. ○ This is subtraction.
	○ The volcano is erupting. ○ The vine is not erupting.
	○ It's a panda from China. ○ It's a lion from Africa.
	○ The daisy has petals. ○ The bicycle has pedals.

Yes or No

Write "yes" or "no."

1. Is a baby young? _____

2. Can a balloon pop? _____

3. Are there twenty days in April? _____

4. Is it okay to steal money? _____

5. Is "hate" an antonym of "love"? _____

6. Do people eat cement? _____

7. Do people eat cereal? _____

8. Is a dime less than a nickel? _____

9. Can an apple dance? _____

10. Can a dictionary be a book? _____

Find the Picture

Write each word on the line under the matching picture.

astronaut			
		astronaut	
gloves			
youngster			
sofa			
money			

camel			
	_____	_____	_____
crystal			
	_____	_____	_____
nostril			
	_____	_____	_____
pineapple			
	_____	_____	_____
reflection			
	_____	_____	_____

Name _____

Circle the Spellings

Circle the correct letters to spell the words correctly.

	(o) / oa	f / (v)	(e) / o	(n) / m	oven
	t / d	ou / or	h / ch		
	z / s	o / a	d / b	i / a	
	r / l	i / oo	o / ow	m / n	
	s / z	o / ee	f / v	a / v	
	g / c	oo / o	mm / nn	a / av	

	wh w	i e	s st	t le	_____
	p b	a e	ne nc	il li	_____
	f t	e a	t b	t le	_____
	f t	o u	m nn	el le	_____
	a u	p pp	le ful		_____

Capital Letters

Circle the words with the missing capital letters. Write the correct form above the word.

Nate
1. (nate,) becca, joel, and i walked to the zoo.

2. mrs. davis' house is next to dogwood park.

3. mary beth likes people to call her just beth.

4. on sunday, uncle charles cooks a big brunch.

5. when i go to mr. smith's sub shop, i always get a meatball sub.

6. we named the class goldfish spike.

7. i would like to travel to china in may.

8. monday is the best day of the week.

Punctuation

Directions: Have students fill in the appropriate ending punctuation. The numbers in parentheses indicate how many punctuation marks need to be added.

1. My home is in Sarasota (1)
    <u>My home is in Sarasota.</u>

2. My sister was born in May (1)
    _____
    _____

3. Linda likes ham and mushrooms in her calzones (1)
    _____
    _____

4. Where did you park your car (1)
    _____
    _____

5. Stop that Mrs. Jones yelled to the rabbit stealing veggies from her garden (4)
    _____
    _____

6. We are getting ready for a puppet show and it is time to make the puppets (1)
    _____
    _____

7.   Who can help me lift these books asked Lily (4)

_____

_____

Nouns

Circle the nouns in the sentences. Note that the number of nouns in each sentence is written at the end of the sentence.

1. (Nostrils) are (part) of the (nose). (3)

2. Melissa had an apple and a banana. (3)

3. The watermelon's seeds are black. (2)

4. Lava is gushing from the erupting volcano. (2)

5. There is an orange ribbon in her hair and a silver bracelet on her wrist. (4)

6. Bees make honey. (2)

7. Adeline is wearing gloves, a hat, and a scarf. (4)

8. Hot wax is dripping down the candle. (2)

Common and Proper Nouns

Circle the common nouns, and draw a box around the proper nouns.

1. (Emma) loves [Batman.]

2. Is Dan a good boxer?

3. The youngsters are eating popsicles.

4. Amos is eating a snack.

5. Picasso was a famous artist.

6. Is the party in March, April, or May?

7. On Monday we went to Oakton.

8. Sara got a love letter.

Nouns and Adjectives

Write down 6 nouns that you see. Then write adjectives to describe each of these nouns.

Adjective	Noun		Adjective	Noun
1. _____ _____			4. _____ _____	
2. _____ _____			5. _____ _____	
3. _____ _____			6. _____ _____	

Changing Nouns

Rewrite the sentences, changing the underlined common nouns to proper nouns.

1. <u>The teacher</u> is reading to her class.
   <u>Miss Sikes is reading to her class.</u>

   _____

2. <u>Our state</u> is the best state!

   _____

   _____

3. <u>They</u> went to <u>the store</u>.

   _____

   _____

4. <u>He</u> loves <u>this holiday</u>.

   _____

   _____

5. <u>She</u> will see <u>a friend</u> on <u>a weekday</u>.

_____

_____

Subject and Predicate Verb Tense

Read the sentences. Draw one line under the subject and two lines under the predicate. Then mark whether the verb is in the present, past or future tense.

1. <u>Donald and his younger brother</u> <u><u>jogged down the street.</u></u>

    present/past/future

2. Mother welcomes Rachel and Gerald.

    present/past/future

3. Elizabeth will come with us.

    present/past/future

4. The whole class complimented the principal's necktie.

    present/past/future

5. Uncle Dan likes jokes.

    present/past/future

6. Tyson bicycled home.

    present/past/future

7. Dad will label our lunches.

    present/past/future

8. Large lobsters swim in the sea.

    present/past/future

9. Gabriel orders an appetizer.

    present/past/future

10. Anita will travel to Africa.

    present/past/future

Adjectives

Circle the nouns, and then draw a line from the adjective to the noun it describes. Some sentences may have more than one adjective and noun.

1. A brown rabbit hopped into the yard.

2. A shiny spaceship is floating in the sky.

3. The baby waved its tiny hand in the air.

4. The full moon is a wonderful light at night.

5. The red bird flew to the large nest.

6. The enormous troll frightened the nervous knights.

7. White snowflakes float down from the gray sky.

8. Twinkling stars dot the sky.

9. Her green eyes sparkled with delight.

10. He rode a blue motorcycle.

Compound Words

Choose a word from the box to make a compound word.

come	fly	side	down
ball	apple	devil	melon

1. dare + _____ = _____

2. touch + _____ = _____

3. dragon + _____ = _____

4. pine + _____ = _____

5. water + _____ = _____

6. cannon + _____ = _____

7. out + _____ = _____

8. be + _____ = _____

Write a sentence or silly story in which you use at least one of the compound words you just made.

_____

_____

_____

_____

_____

_____

_____

_____

_____

_____

_____

_____

Match the Words: Synonyms

Choose a synonym from the box for each word listed below, and write it on the line.

scared	feel	giant	magnificent	bicycle
fast	awful	bad	soil	mad

1. touch _____

2. wonderful _____

3. enormous _____

4. afraid _____

5. dirt _____

6. evil _____

7. terrible _____

8. angry _____

9. bike _____

10. quickly _____

Match the Words: Antonyms

Choose an antonym from the box for each word listed below, and write it on the line.

ugly	together	love	above	simple
fact	vertical	strange	compliment	old

1. normal _____

2. young _____

3. handsome _____

4. below _____

5. apart _____

6. difficult _____

7. hate _____

8. horizontal _____

9. insult _____

10. fiction _____

Fill in the Blank

The words in bold print sound the same, but they do not mean the same thing. Fill in the blanks so the sentences make sense.

1. **one/won**

   _____One_____ person _____won_____ the prize.

2. **pair/pear**

   He ate a _____ with his _____ of hands.

3. **son/sun**

   Her _____ is soaking up the _____.

4. **Some/sum**

   _____ of these numbers have a _____ of six when added together.

5. **weak/week**

   I was sick last _____, and I felt very _____.

Spelling Lessons 1–5

Write the best word from the box to complete each sentence.

quickly	neatly	ugly	jelly	chilly
slowly	funny	angry	empty	mommy
daddy	happy	pretty	grumpy	alphabet

1. I am not fond of putting words in order of the _____.

2. Please put your clothes away _____.

3. I like _____ with my toast.

4. She is a _____ little pony.

5. I move _____ in the morning.

6. I am so _____ that you got an "A."

7. Her _____ is my uncle.

8. I like to watch _____ animal movies.

Write the best word from the box to complete each sentence.

quickly	neatly	ugly	jelly	chilly
slowly	funny	angry	empty	mommy
daddy	happy	pretty	grumpy	alphabet

9. Are you _____ that I broke the lamp?

10. Will you _____ the dishwasher?

11. What an _____ troll!

12. It is too _____ not to wear a coat.

13. Can you come _____ to help me?

14. Her _____ is my aunt.

15. I am kind of _____ when I am sleepy.

Spelling Lessons 6–10

Write the best word from the box to complete each sentence.

knight	might	high	right	frightened
light	bright	crying	pry	why
nearby	trying	sky	drying	kingdom

1. King Alfred cared about the people in his

    _____.

2. Look! What's that up in the _____?

3. The _____ wore armor and rode a horse.

4. Are you _____ to be alone in the dark?

5. I have been _____ to call you all day.

6. It _____ be time to go to bed.

7. I hope you are not _____ over spilled milk.

Write the best word from the box to complete each sentence.

knight	might	high	right	frightened
light	bright	crying	pry	why
nearby	trying	sky	drying	kingdom

8. The sun is so _____ I have to wear sunglasses.

9. It is _____, so I can carry it.

10. Can you jump as _____ as the basketball goal?

11. The clothes are _____ in the dryer.

12. That is the _____ thing to do.

13. I don't know _____ she is crying.

14. She had to _____ the stuck door open.

15. I live _____ the park.

Spelling Lessons 11–15

Write the best word from the box to complete each sentence.

field	piece	shield	thief	kitties
achieve	relief	grief	yield	movie
niece	cookies	ladies	babies	water

1. I do not like to go under _____.

2. How many _____ have you eaten?

3. The _____ met for tea.

4. My _____ is named Amy.

5. How many doll _____ do you own?

6. I like to go to the _____ theater to see films.

7. The farmer will plow the _____.

8. A triangle shaped sign at the intersection means _____.

Write the best word from the box to complete each sentence.

field	piece	shield	thief	kitties
achieve	relief	grief	yield	movie
niece	cookies	ladies	babies	water

9.   Could I please have a _____ of pie?

10.   What a _____ to get some help with my homework.

11. The knight used a _____ to protect himself.

12. That _____ stole my money.

13. How many baby _____ did your cat have?

14. Did you _____ an "A" on your report card?

15. She cried and was full of _____ when her dog died.

Spelling Lessons 16–20

Write the best word from the box to complete each sentence.

yelled	yarn	yellow	yes	myth
symbol	system	cry	frying	satisfy
yawn	sticky	lying	energy	edge

1. Stay away from the _____ of the cliff!

2. My fingers are _____ from the glue.

3. Please don't _____! We can fix the broken lamp.

4. I would like a game box _____ for my TV.

5. What is the _____ for the sound of schwa?

6. Our teacher will tell us a Greek _____.

7. _____, I am going with you to the fair.

8. Is the sun _____ in your picture?

Write the best word from the box to complete each sentence.

yelled	yarn	yellow	yes	myth
symbol	system	cry	frying	satisfy
yawn	sticky	lying	energy	edge

9. My mom knitted a sweater with yellow
_____ for me.

10. I started to _____ when I felt sleepy.

11. She _____ across the field to her sister.

12. Are you _____ chicken for supper?

13. Did you get enough food to _____ you?

14. I am too tired, and I do not have the _____
to fix your lunch.

15. Do not start _____ to your mother.

Spelling Lessons 21–25

Write the best word from the box to complete each sentence.

turtle	bundle	pickle	shuffle	cattle
label	angel	gravel	jewel	fiction
education	inspection	motion	question	schwa

1. ə is the symbol for the word _____.

2. May I ask you a _____?

3. I have a pet box _____.

4. The bright _____ in her ring is shiny.

5. Can you put a _____ on the box?

6. The farmer's _____ ran to get fed.

7. Can you _____ the deck of cards?

8. I like a dill _____ with my sandwich.

Write the best word from the box to complete each sentence.

turtle	bundle	pickle	shuffle	cattle
label	angel	gravel	jewel	fiction
education	inspection	motion	question	schwa

9. I am trying to pick up a _____ of sticks for the fire.

10. Did you have wings with your _____ costume?

11. I like to read _____ books.

12. I fell on the _____ driveway and cut my hands.

13. It is important to get an _____.

14. The _____ of the boat made Sir Gus seasick.

15. Our clean room passed mom's _____.

Name _____

Alphabetical Order

Write these words in alphabetical order.

hood	touch	fly	dragon	come
pine	water	ball	apple	melon

1. _____

2. _____

3. _____

4. _____

5. _____

6. _____

7. _____

8. _____

9. _____

10. _____

Alphabetical Order

Write these words in alphabetical order.

enormous	magnificent	wicked	bicycle	hastily
awful	terrible	giant	jealous	

1. _____

2. _____

3. _____

4. _____

5. _____

6. _____

7. _____

8. _____

9. _____

CORE KNOWLEDGE LANGUAGE ARTS

SERIES EDITOR-IN-CHIEF
E. D. Hirsch, Jr.

PRESIDENT
Linda Bevilacqua

EDITORIAL STAFF
Carolyn Gosse, Senior Editor - Preschool
Khara Turnbull, Materials Development Manager
Michelle L. Warner, Senior Editor - Listening & Learning

Mick Anderson
Robin Blackshire
Maggie Buchanan
Paula Coyner
Sue Fulton
Sara Hunt
Erin Kist
Robin Luecke
Rosie McCormick
Cynthia Peng
Liz Pettit
Ellen Sadler
Deborah Samley
Diane Auger Smith
Sarah Zelinke

DESIGN AND GRAPHICS STAFF
Scott Ritchie, Creative Director

Kim Berrall
Michael Donegan
Liza Greene
Matt Leech
Bridget Moriarty
Lauren Pack

CONSULTING PROJECT MANAGEMENT SERVICES
ScribeConcepts.com

ADDITIONAL CONSULTING SERVICES
Ang Blanchette
Dorrit Green
Carolyn Pinkerton

ACKNOWLEDGMENTS

These materials are the result of the work, advice, and encouragement of numerous individuals over many years. Some of those singled out here already know the depth of our gratitude; others may be surprised to find themselves thanked publicly for help they gave quietly and generously for the sake of the enterprise alone. To helpers named and unnamed we are deeply grateful.

CONTRIBUTORS TO EARLIER VERSIONS OF THESE MATERIALS

Susan B. Albaugh, Kazuko Ashizawa, Nancy Braier, Kathryn M. Cummings, Michelle De Groot, Diana Espinal, Mary E. Forbes, Michael L. Ford, Ted Hirsch, Danielle Knecht, James K. Lee, Diane Henry Leipzig, Martha G. Mack, Liana Mahoney, Isabel McLean, Steve Morrison, Juliane K. Munson, Elizabeth B. Rasmussen, Laura Tortorelli, Rachael L. Shaw, Sivan B. Sherman, Miriam E. Vidaver, Catherine S. Whittington, Jeannette A. Williams

We would like to extend special recognition to Program Directors Matthew Davis and Souzanne Wright who were instrumental to the early development of this program.

SCHOOLS

We are truly grateful to the teachers, students, and administrators of the following schools for their willingness to field test these materials and for their invaluable advice: Capitol View Elementary, Challenge Foundation Academy (IN), Community Academy Public Charter School, Lake Lure Classical Academy, Lepanto Elementary School, New Holland Core Knowledge Academy, Paramount School of Excellence, Pioneer Challenge Foundation Academy, New York City PS 26R (The Carteret School), PS 30X (Wilton School), PS 50X (Clara Barton School), PS 96Q, PS 102X (Joseph O. Loretan), PS 104Q (The Bays Water), PS 214K (Michael Friedsam), PS 223Q (Lyndon B. Johnson School), PS 308K (Clara Cardwell), PS 333Q (Goldie Maple Academy), Sequoyah Elementary School, South Shore Charter Public School, Spartanburg Charter School, Steed Elementary School, Thomas Jefferson Classical Academy, Three Oaks Elementary, West Manor Elementary.

And a special thanks to the CKLA Pilot Coordinators Anita Henderson, Yasmin Lugo-Hernandez, and Susan Smith, whose suggestions and day-to-day support to teachers using these materials in their classrooms was critical.

Core Knowledge®

CREDITS